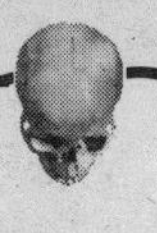

A WRITER'S NOTEBOOK:

HOW TO WRITE SCARY STORIES

A WRITER'S NOTEBOOK:

HOW TO WRITE SCARY STORIES

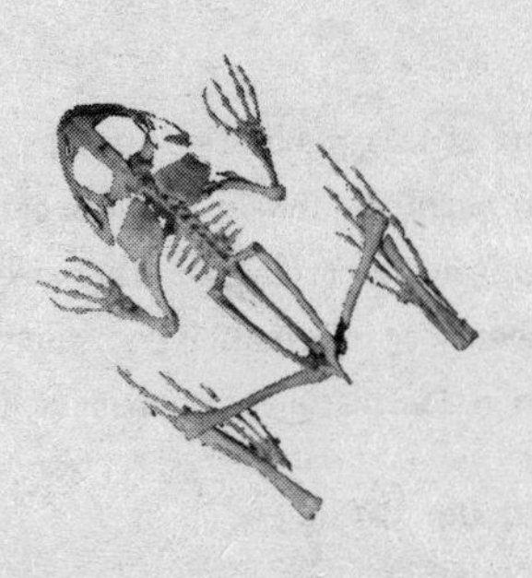

Kimberly Weinberger

SCHOLASTIC INC.
New York Toronto London Auckland Sydney
Mexico City New Delhi Hong Kong Buenos Aires

ISBN 0-439-29146-1

12 11 10 9 8 7 6 5 4 3 2 1 2 3 4 5 6/0

Printed in the U.S.A. 40

First printing, October 2001

Ready for a Scare?

Are you the kind of person who loves a good scary story? Do you enjoy the tingles that run up and down your spine when you know something creepy is lurking inside the pages of a book? Do you ever wish that you could write those chilling stories yourself?

If you answered yes to these questions, then you've come to the right place! The notebook you now hold in your hands is brimming with helpful advice and tips on how to craft spooky and suspenseful tales. Best of all, there are loads of blank pages for you to fill with your own stories, thoughts, ideas — and nightmares!

No need to worry about rules or grades here. This notebook is for you and you alone. So go ahead and write in it whenever and wherever you choose. The only thing you might risk is scaring yourself silly with your own stories.

And that's the idea, right?

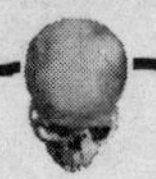

Getting Started

To get yourself in the writing mode, you'll need to cover a few basics first. For example, do you prefer to write with a pen or pencil on paper? Or perhaps a keyboard and computer screen are more your style?

Try your hand at different writing tools, and see which feels best to you. Note the tools below, and jot down your thoughts. A little experimenting will help you decide which to choose.

The Perfect Spot

Though you may place your characters in dank dungeons or darkened tombs, you yourself should find someplace a little more comfortable to create your scary masterpieces. Some writers prefer utter silence and a clean desk to get their creative juices flowing. Others may pop in a favorite CD and sit happily among stacks of books and papers while they work.

You may find that you enjoy writing outside when the weather is warm. Once the temperature drops, gazing through a window might take the place of being in the great outdoors.

Wherever you choose to write, be sure it's comfortable and has plenty of light. Then you're ready to begin!

Story Time

As an aspiring writer, you may have heard that you should try to write something every day. This is good advice, though not always practical for students with extra-busy schedules. Trying to squeeze in some writing time while sitting in the back of math class or during soccer practice can only lead to trouble. So what's a writer to do?

For starters, don't be hard on yourself. Try setting reasonable writing goals for a week and see how you do. If you can only manage a few sentences on Monday, don't despair. A great idea for a hauntingly good story may strike you on Tuesday, and you'll find yourself wishing there were more than seven days in a week!

Morning, noon, or night, the choice of when to write is up to you. Only you can know what times work best. When writing a tense and frightening scene in a graveyard, the dark of night may be the only time that gets you in the proper mood. Or maybe the harsh light of day helps cast shadows that inspire your scary side.

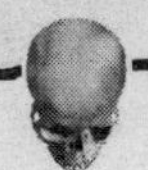

Use these lines to describe what you think may be your favorite times and places to write your scary stories. Why do they work for you?

A Scary Sight

Writers of scary stories may describe heart-stopping scenes of terror, eerie incidents of horror, and downright chilling displays of evil with the greatest of ease. But what's the one thing that can make even these fearless authors hide beneath their covers?

The blank page.

That's right. A simple blank sheet of paper. Or for the more technologically advanced, a blank computer screen with that endlessly blinking cursor.

What to write about is the eternal question that all writers face. Judging from the numbers of bookstores and libraries in the world, it seems there must be a never-ending supply of stories to tell. So why is deciding what to write about such a challenge? Where do writers get their ideas?

The answer to this question is: anywhere and everywhere (not a very helpful answer, but in fact true). In the shower, on the bus, during lunch, after dinner, at three o'clock in the morning — these are just a few of the times and places that great ideas can strike.

For this reason, many writers keep a small notebook or journal by their side at all times. They know that no matter how great an idea might be, it may be difficult to remember unless it's written down the moment it's born. So get into the habit of carrying a notebook and writing in it when inspiration hits. You'll soon discover that the world is filled with story ideas just waiting for you to recognize them.

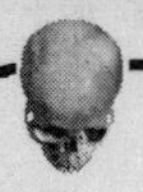

Picture This

Think of a cluttered and dusty attic. Picture it in your mind, and write what you see on these pages.

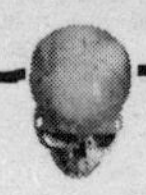

Remember Your Spooky Senses

Now that you've described what you saw in that attic, it's time to open your mind to what your other senses can tell you.

When you read words on a page, you're using your sense of sight. But the right words can involve your other four senses as well. Words can convey sounds, tastes, smells, and textures that bring a single moment in time to life.

As a writer, it's important to always keep these five senses in mind. Become an observer of details in your world. Take notice of your surroundings with all of your senses on high alert. And be sure to jot down your findings in your journal or notebook!

Now picture that old attic once more. Walk through the room in your mind and try answering the following questions.

- **Do the floorboards creak and groan when you step on them?**
- **Can you see tiny specks of dust hovering in a ray of late afternoon sunshine?**
- **Does the smell of stale mothballs hang heavy in the air?**

- **Does that canvas tent feel rough and coarse beneath your fingers?**
- **Does your mouth feel dry and gritty as you wipe away layers of dust and cobwebs to reveal a hidden secret?**

Now that you've experienced this place with all of your senses, describe it again. Use the lines below and on pages 16 and 17. Try to create a strong image in the minds of your readers by making them see, hear, taste, smell, and feel the room.

For Sale: A Terrifying Tale

Once you become a true observer of your world, there's no limit to the number of places where you might find great story ideas. Take, for instance, your newspaper. You've probably never looked very closely at your local paper's real estate section. If you did, you might find an ad that looked something like this:

> *FOR SALE: 5 bedroom, 3 bath, historic home. Expansive; situated on scenic lake; owner very motivated — will consider any offer!*

An ordinary person might flip right past this ad without a second thought. But an observant writer such as yourself knows better. This is a story just waiting to be written!

Form a picture of this house in your mind. The ad mentions that it is "historic." What might that mean? Did something sinister happen there many years ago? Can you hear the long dead former owner moaning and weeping as he plots his unspeakable revenge?

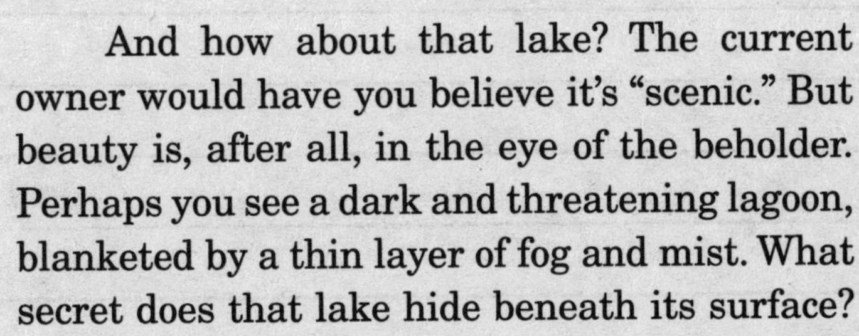

And how about that lake? The current owner would have you believe it's "scenic." But beauty is, after all, in the eye of the beholder. Perhaps you see a dark and threatening lagoon, blanketed by a thin layer of fog and mist. What secret does that lake hide beneath its surface?

Finally, there's the most obvious clue that something is amiss at this house: The owner is "very motivated." Hmmm. Now what would make this owner consider "any offer" for such a large lakeside house? Could it be that evil walks its halls?

As you can see, your imagination will play an important part in turning everyday newspaper items into hair-raising tales. Use the ad on page 18, or choose one from your own newspaper, and try to create a short story. Write your story on the following pages.

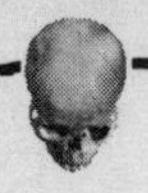

A Ghostly Graveyard

Here's an unsettling piece of news from a small-town newspaper.

Residents of this sleepy New England village are today mourning the senseless vandalism that has turned a local graveyard into a chaotic rubble of overturned and broken headstones. More than 30 graves have been dug up or otherwise disturbed. Police have no leads in the case at this time.

There are few more classically creepy places than a graveyard. Obviously, the vandalism in this news item is a case for the police. But with a little creativity, you might come up with culprits far stranger than a group of lawless thugs.

Suppose a magician unearthed those graves to aid in his practice of dark magic? Or perhaps a ghostly tenant of one of the graves managed to escape its dark prison six feet below the ground? What would happen if several ghosts emerged from the graveyard?

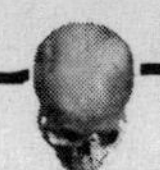

Let your imagination run wild as you write a story about this news item — or one of your own choosing — here and on page 24.

Photo Gallery

Have you ever heard the saying "A picture is worth a thousand words"? Writers everywhere know that statement to be true. That's why many of them keep a collection of interesting photographs on hand.

Choose a photograph and check out the expression on a person's face. Does the person seem sad or angry? Do the eyes seem to follow you? Or perhaps a forced smile is covering up some deep, dark secret?

Think about what might have happened the morning that the picture was taken. What did the person do later that afternoon? Or the following day? Study the backgrounds of each photograph to gather more detailed information.

Photos of places, animals, or unusual objects are also worth collecting. Create a history for what you see, and you'll have the makings of a story in no time.

Look Inside

In order to write truly scary stories, it's important to know how to tap into common fears that all of us might share. To do that, just look inside yourself. What things frighten you the most?

One of the first childhood fears that might come to mind is fear of the dark. Though you may have outgrown your night-light, there is a part of you that will always remember that creepy feeling of not being able to see what's around you.

Think back to what it felt like to be in your room as a small child. You were all alone in the dark. Was that a rustling you heard in the corner? Did you squint into the inky blackness, seeing only a shapeless, hulking figure? If only you could turn on the light, you could see what was hiding there. But that would mean stepping out of your bed.

Try to come up with a list of ten things that can make the hairs on the back of your neck stand on end. Perhaps it's the beady eyes of a rat or the slither of a snake. Or maybe it's a more general fear of closed-in spaces, or even death. Write your answers here and on page 28, explaining briefly why each fear makes you shiver.

What a Nightmare!

Though they're not much fun when you're having one, nightmares can be a great help to a writer of scary stories. A particularly vivid bad dream may bring to light some unknown fears that stalk your subconscious mind, giving you a glimpse of a strong story idea that only you can create.

Because dreams have a tendency to fade as the day goes on, it's a good idea to write down all that you remember about them the moment you awake. Keep a pen and some paper at your bedside to record the details. What was frightening about the dream? Were you in physical danger? Was someone chasing you? Did he or she — or it — catch you? Then what happened?

Think back to the scariest dream you've ever had, and describe it here and on pages 30 and 31.

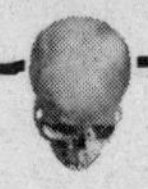

Creepy Characters

Now that you've taken a closer look at your own fears and nightmares, it's time to turn your focus away from yourself. Try to assume a different identity, and watch the stories flow!

Consider the following list of characters. Get inside their minds — if you dare! How would they think, feel, and behave? Choose one or more, and write a story on pages 33 and 34.

- **A teenager accidentally locked inside a deserted school**
- **A hiker lost at night on a desolate mountain**
- **A ghost who will stop at nothing to guard his home from snooping visitors**
- **A fisherman whose boat is adrift in a lonely, foggy sea**

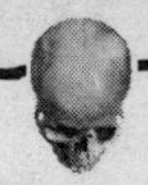

A Strong and Spooky Start

So, you've now gotten the hang of where to write, when to write, and what to write. Can you guess the next step in your quest to become a scary story writer? That's right — it's how to write.

To begin at the beginning, an attention-grabbing opening sentence is a surefire way to pull readers into your story. Once they're hooked, they'll want to read more to find out what happens next.

Take a look at the following sentence.

> *One summer day, Sam went to live in a haunted house.*

What can we say about this sentence? For starters, it's a bit on the boring side. True, it does set up a character and a situation, thereby giving important information to the reader. But is there a better way to open this story?

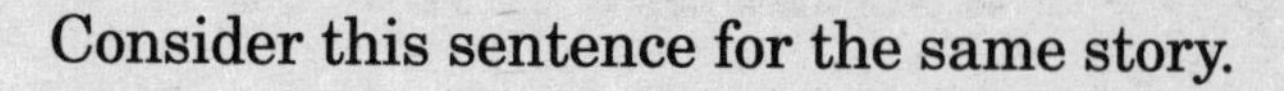

Consider this sentence for the same story.

Though it was the hottest day of the summer, Sam felt chilled to the bone the moment he stepped into his new house.

What's different about this version? While it doesn't come right out and say Sam's house is haunted, it does include the action of Sam stepping into his house and his physical feeling of being cold once inside. Including a physical action or movement and touching on a detail of feeling (remember those five senses!) can make for an outstanding opening sentence.

Sight, smell, sound, thought, and speech are also wonderful elements that can be used in first lines. For example, here's that opening line again, this time using thought to grab the reader's interest:

What a creepy place, Sam thought as he stepped inside the dark, chilly hallway of his new house.

Think of other ways to open this story, using speech, sight, smell, or sound to add some instant interest. Write your thoughts at the top of the next page.

Do not feel intimidated by trying to come up with the world's greatest opening line. You might find it easier to use any generic opening sentence just to get your story underway. Once you've got the story rolling — or even finished — you can revisit your opening and see how you might change it for the better.

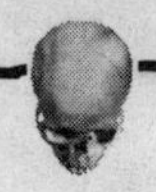

Scary Story Starters

Here are a few story starters designed to give you goose bumps. Choose as many as you like, and continue writing on these pages.

I had seen the young girl's ghost on the stairs more than three times before I finally decided to tell someone about it.

Mike took the shortcut through the woods to his house nearly every day. But on Thursday, he never made it home.

"Please don't sit next to me," Maria muttered to herself as the strange, hollow-eyed man made his way toward her on the bus.

Now You Try

See if you can come up with one or more exciting opening sentences based on the story summaries below.

On a small farm, a scarecrow comes to life and plays eerie tricks on the farm's inhabitants. Can the family stop it before its pranks turn deadly?

A lonely young boy meets a friend while playing in the woods near his home. But he soon makes a shocking discovery — his new playmate is actually a boy who died in those woods more than twenty years earlier!

A teenage girl is nearly killed when she falls through the ice of a frozen pond. As she slowly recovers in her home, she begins to hear voices calling to her from the pond's icy depths. Someone, or something, wants her back in its frigid grasp.

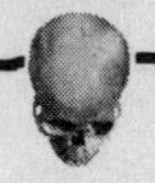

Choosing a Voice

Before an author begins to write anything, he or she must first decide who is telling the story. This is called the story's *point of view*.

One possibility is to write in the *first person*. This means that the narrator of the story uses *I* and *we* throughout. In other words, one of the characters is telling the story to the reader. For example:

> *I don't remember much of that winter. I can see myself standing in the mud at Jason's funeral, wondering how my best friend could be gone. I guess I should have known, even then, that I would be next on the monster's list.*

A second option for point of view is the *third person* narrative. When using this style, the writer becomes an all-knowing narrator. The characters in the story are referred to as *he, she*, and *they*. The following is an example of this style.

Meg discovered that she had magical powers at the age of four. She learned to use them wisely and to hide them from those who wouldn't understand. Then, on her sixteenth birthday, she met an evil force that threatened her very existence.

Whichever point of view you choose, it's important to stick with it throughout your story. Switching between different narrators can become confusing, so always be consistent.

Try experimenting with different narrative styles in your writing. You may find that writing in the first person makes your story more personal, placing the reader inside the mind of a frightened character.

On the other hand, writing in the third person can allow you to inform the reader of certain dangers or threats of which the main character isn't aware. This creates tension for your readers, as they wish they could warn the character before it's too late!

Bring It to Life

Here's a challenging point-of-view activity: Choose an object from the list below. Try to give it feelings, thoughts, and opinions. Then write a scary story from the object's point of view.

- **A sorcerer's wand**
- **A grave's headstone**
- **A clown puppet**
- **A buried skeleton**
- **A fun-house mirror**

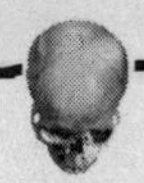

Snowed In

Picture the following scene: A young boy and his parents are snowed in at their mountain cabin. The boy is frightened when he hears a soft moaning coming from somewhere inside the cabin walls. His mother says not to worry, telling him it's only the wind. His father heads out into the storm to find some firewood and does not return.

Using a first person point of view, try to write a paragraph or two for each of the characters in this scene. What is the boy feeling? What thoughts are going through the mother's head? What is the father doing? And finally, what about the thing that is making the moaning noise?

Try to remember the most frightening scene from one of your favorite scary books, TV shows, or movies. Retell the scene here, using both first person and third person points of view. You might want to use the first person style more than once, so that a different character tells the story each time.

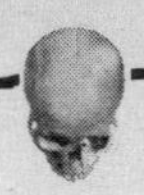

Character Creations

No matter what type of story you're writing, you're going to need characters to drive the action. These characters can be people, animals, aliens, monsters, or even objects. All they need to become worthy characters is personality.

As a writer, you must get to know your characters inside and out. What are their deepest fears and darkest secrets? What are their good points and bad points? Just like real people, your characters should come alive in your mind and on the page.

One trick writers use is to base their characters on people they actually know. You might combine traits from several real people to make a single fictional personality.

Can you think of any people in your life who might make great heroes or heroines or even ghosts or monsters? Start a list here.

Good Characters...

Have you ever met a 100 percent perfect person? Someone who always does and says exactly the right thing and never makes a wrong decision? Chances are, you haven't. That's because we are all only human and are bound to make mistakes.

It can be helpful to remember this fact when you're creating your own characters. People can become stubborn, angry, or jealous. They can lose their temper and annoy others. All in all, though, they can still be good.

Creating perfect characters is, in a word, boring. So allow your characters to have some human flaws. When a reader is able to sympathize with a character, he or she will become that much more involved and concerned when that character is placed in grave danger.

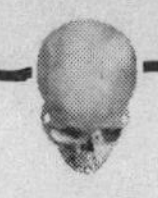

. . . and Bad Characters

In a scary story, there's almost always some sort of "bad" character. It can be a ghost, a witch, a demon, a monster, an animal, an insect, or anything else your imagination can dream up. The important thing is that this character strikes fear in the hearts of the rest of the characters in the story — and of your readers!

As with your good characters, you'll want to learn all you can about the bad ones. Why do they do the evil things they do? What is their goal? How far would they go to reach it? Though you may not actually answer these questions in your story, they're helpful in letting you decide how your character should behave.

Here are some questions to consider when creating any character, good or bad.

- **What is the character's family life like? Does the character have siblings? Parents? Children?**
- **What does the character like or love? What does the character dislike or hate?**
- **Is the character hiding any secrets?**
- **Does he or she have any special abilities or talents?**
- **What has happened in the character's past to make the person the way he or she is today?**

The Hidden Monster

Sometimes a frightening story can be made even more disturbing by keeping the danger under wraps. In other words, by not unveiling the monster, ghost, or other evil character until the very end (and sometimes not even then), you can create a great deal of tension in your story.

Think about it this way: While a slavering monster with huge fangs can be truly scary, the sound of slow, trudging footsteps overhead can be even more so. Threatening your characters with some unseen danger keeps your readers at the same disadvantage — what is it, and when will it finally show itself?

Try writing a story with an unseen scary character here. Have a clear picture in your mind of what the character is, but don't actually describe it until the end.

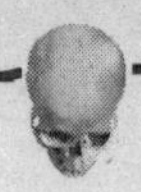

Eerie Expressions

Although appearance is definitely not everything when it comes to characters, it can be a good way to convey information about an individual. Body language, facial expressions, and clothing all combine to create a picture of a personality even before the character has spoken a single word.

For example, how might you describe a suspicious man with a somewhat sinister air about him? Would he have small, beady eyes that dart this way and that? Would his mouth be twisted in a permanent sneer? Would he wear a long, dark overcoat that could hide many secrets?

Consider the following list of characters. Choose one or more, and describe the personality using only physical actions and appearance.

- **A frightened girl**
- **An angry ghost**
- **A nervous dog**
- **A sad and lonely woman**

Spine-tingling Speech

One of the most important elements in moving your story along is dialogue, or conversation between characters. Strong, well-written dialogue can often take the place of long-winded narrative, allowing you to share information with readers in a straightforward and easy manner.

Having a conversation with someone is easy. Writing a realistic conversation is not. Listen to an actual conversation. You'll find that much of what we say is not very important. Take, for instance, the following piece of dialogue:

"Hey, Cheryl," said John.
"Hey, what's up?" said Cheryl.
"Nothing," said John. "What are you doing now?"
"Nothing," said Cheryl.
"Well, I was thinking of heading over to the old Miller place," said John.
"What for?" asked Cheryl.
"I've heard that it might be haunted," answered John.
"Really?" said Cheryl.
"Yeah," said John. "Want to come with me and find out?"

Obviously, the fact that the old Miller place is rumored to be haunted is the most important part of John and Cheryl's conversation. But who could stay awake during the first part of this dialogue to find that out? To keep the interest of a reader, try mixing narrative and dialogue together.

> *By the time John caught up with Cheryl, he was nearly out of breath. As the two walked together, Cheryl noticed that John seemed excited and anxious.*
> *"I was thinking of heading over to the old Miller place," said John, trying to sound casual.*
> *"What for?" asked Cheryl.*
> *John gave her a nervous grin. "I've heard that it might be haunted!" he whispered.*
> *"Really?" said Cheryl, trying hard to keep a straight face.*
> *"Yeah," John answered eagerly. "Want to come with me and find out?"*

Omitting the boring parts of everyday conversation leaves more room for intriguing information. And that makes for better storytelling!

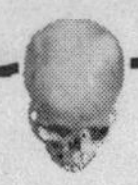

How We Speak

What's the best way to tell whether your dialogue sounds realistic? Read it aloud. If the words sound stiff or unnatural to your ear, they're sure to sound the same way to the person reading your story.

Learn to pay close attention to your own conversations and those of people around you (without becoming an eavesdropper, of course!). For example, you'll find that instead of saying "I am scared" or "He is lost," people are more likely to say, "I'm scared," "He's lost." Combining short words into contractions is a common habit of everyday speech.

Learning to write realistic and interesting dialogue takes practice, practice, and more practice. See if you can write a conversation for one or more of the following situations.

- **Two children alone in a house during a blackout**
- **A group of people trapped inside a haunted mansion**
- **A young girl befriending the ghost of a boy who died long ago**

Petrifying Plots

It has twists and turns, thrills, chills, and surprises. What is it? The plot!

The plot is your main story. It should flow smoothly from start to finish, with no unanswered questions at the end. And just as your characters need flaws to keep them interesting, so your plot should include at least one problem to keep a reader's attention.

Scary stories in particular call for dangerous situations that place the main characters in jeopardy. The hero or heroine must face a major obstacle or two in order to find safety and peace of mind. The reason for this is obvious: Reading a story where everything goes as planned and no one has any problems will put your readers to sleep in no time!

There are three main pieces to every plot:

1. the setup

2. the action

3. the ending

Setting the Scene

The *setup*, as the word implies, involves setting up the situation. When does the story take place, who and where are the characters, and what is their main problem?

The *where* and *when* are also known as the *setting*. Are we in a haunted castle in the eighteenth century? On a hostile alien planet in the year 3010? On a doomed vacation last week in California?

Here's a list of various settings. Choose one or more or make up your own, and write a story based on that setting on pages 64 and 65.

- **A deserted ghost town in Colorado during the late 1800s**
- **Transylvania on Halloween night in the fifteenth century**
- **A distant planet inhabited by dangerous aliens in the far future**
- **A darkened forest in present-day Virginia**
- **Massachusetts during the Salem witch trials**

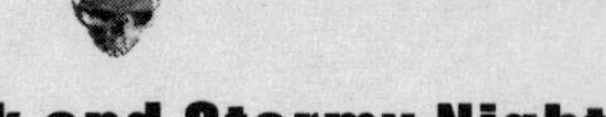

It Was a Dark and Stormy Night

While basically any time and place can be scary in the hands of a skilled writer, it is still true that certain settings lend themselves more easily to frightening situations.

One of the most often used times is the dark of night. There's something about a pitch-black evening that seems to add a sense of mystery and fear to a terrifying tale. We can't see as much or as far as we can during daylight hours. This puts us at a disadvantage when creatures may be creeping, crawling, and slithering about unseen. As the saying goes, "Things that go bump in the night can be the most frightening of all."

Cold, bleak winters and ferocious storms are also common settings for scary stories. When even the very elements of the earth seem to be turning against your characters, a sense of doom and gloom comes through on every page.

Of course, equally scary stories can take place on days filled with sunshine and flowers, too. But more often than not, the setting reflects the mood of the story in all its frightening detail.

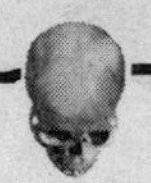

Try your hand at coming up with a scary story in a nighttime setting. How does the darkness affect your characters and their situation? Write your story here and on pages 68 and 69.

Time to Take Action

Now that you've got your setup in place, you're ready to move on to the main part of your plot — the *action*.

The action is the main body of the story. It's where your characters face whatever dangers you've thrown their way. They try to overcome obstacles, deal with their fears, seek out help, and basically work their way through the maze of problems you've created for them.

This section is also a place for you to introduce still more obstacles and setbacks, if you care to. Let your characters' personalities grow and change. Test their courage, and find out how good — or bad — they really are.

The action of your story should move along at a steady pace, not so slowly that the reader loses interest and not so fast that he or she can't keep up.

The Turning Point

The big payoff in any story comes at the *turning point*. That's the moment when the problem is solved, the danger is defeated, and everything is made clear. Also known as the *climax*, this is the scene that pulls all (or almost all) loose ends together. As it does so, it signals the end of the action section of your plot.

As you write your story, you may plan exactly when you'd like the turning point to take place. That's fine, but remember to be flexible as your story unfolds. You may find that the action takes you somewhere unexpected, and things may not turn out as you originally planned.

Keep your mind open to any and all possibilities. You may surprise yourself with an even better tale!

Think of a favorite scary book you've read or movie you've seen. Do you know what the turning point was? Re-create that scene here in your own words, or write one based on a story of your own.

All's Well That Ends Well

Once you've reached the turning point in your story, you'll want to tie up any remaining loose ends. As you may have guessed, this part is called the *ending*.

Before bringing your plot to a close, read through the story once more. You might want to revisit some events that occurred at the beginning. Connecting your characters' situation at the start to their situation at the end is called coming *full circle*. This technique, also known as *closure*, gives your story a sense of satisfying completeness.

Above all, be sure not to leave any unanswered questions. If one of your minor characters went to hide beneath his bed on page 2, don't forget to get him out by the end of the story. You may have forgotten about him, but your readers haven't!

Final Words

The last few sentences of your story can be as important as your opening lines. As all writers know, those final words contain the last thoughts readers will go away with when they have finished reading.

Some writers use their last paragraph to hint at the future of one or more of their characters. This can be a comfort to readers who've grown to like the world you've created and want it to continue beyond the last page. If your characters have faced great danger and heart-stopping situations, readers will be relieved to know that the future is brighter for these fictional personalities.

World-class endings call for just the right words. They should create a sense of satisfaction in the reader, bringing closure to the story in a few neat phrases.

Take a look at some classic books, and read their endings. See how the authors choose their words to create that feeling of finality. Let them be an inspiration for your own writing!

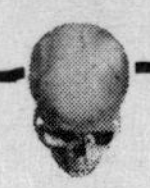

What's So Funny?

Is there a place for humor in a spooky story? Of course there is! Humor can provide a much-needed break from the tension of a bone-chilling scene. Plus it serves another useful purpose: Readers can be soothed into a false sense of security when the story turns comic, only to be doubly shocked when something horrifying bursts in on the very next page!

Can you write a scary scene that contains a humorous moment? Try creating fear at the beginning, then lightening the mood for a moment. Just when all seems safe, let the hair-raising feeling return in full force!

A Touch of Mystery

For many authors, the concept of a mystery often goes hand in hand with writing a scary story. There's nothing like that certain sense of suspense to turn a frightening tale into a real page-turner.

To add a touch of mystery to your scary story, you'll want to include three elements: clues, suspects, and *red herrings*.

Like pieces of a puzzle, clues come together to form a clear picture of a situation. A single clue on its own will not provide the answer to the mystery. But as they add up, a series of well-placed clues will lead the reader straight to the creepy culprit.

If you want to keep your readers guessing, it's a good idea to throw in several suspects. You may know in your head that the strange happenings at the Mansion of Mystery are due to the ghost of the original owner. But your readers don't need to know that until the end of the story. So why not add a suspicious-looking handyman, a nosy neighbor, and other likely suspects to the mysterious mix? The extra suspense will keep readers guessing till the last page.

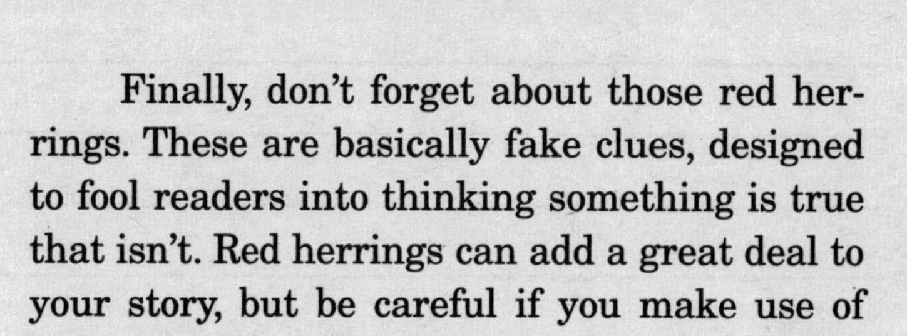

Finally, don't forget about those red herrings. These are basically fake clues, designed to fool readers into thinking something is true that isn't. Red herrings can add a great deal to your story, but be careful if you make use of them. You'll need to explain what they really were by the end of the story.

Here are a few mystery titles. Choose your favorite, or make up one of your own. Then try writing a suspenseful, spooky mystery on the following pages.

- **The Mystery of the Attic Ghost**
- **The Case of the Wandering Werewolf**
- **The Secret of the Witch's Brew**
- **The Mystery of the Lonely Lagoon**

Read All About It

If you want to be a truly exceptional writer of scary stories, you can't skip one very important step: reading!

Trying to be a writer without also being an avid reader is a little like trying to be a chef without tasting any food. You need to experience what great writing is all about before you can tackle your own tales.

Ask your parents, teachers, or a librarian to recommend some must-reads in the scary story genre. Or simply go to the library or bookstore yourself and start browsing. Whether you choose traditional classics or more modern spooky stories, you're sure to find inspiration in the pages of a favorite book.

Here's the start of a reading list of some tremendously terrifying titles. Add more of your own favorites as you find them.

Behind the Attic Wall by Sylvia Cassedy
The Children of Green Knowe by Lucy Boston
Count Karlstein by Philip Pullman
The Dollhouse Murders by Betty Ren Wright
The Ghost of Fossil Glen by Cynthia C. DeFelice

The Halloween Tree by Ray Bradbury
The House With a Clock in Its Walls by John Bellairs
Jade Green: A Ghost Story by Phyllis Reynolds Naylor
Knee Knock Rise by Natalie Babbitt
The Legend of Sleepy Hollow by Washington Irving
Midnight Magic by Avi
Scary Stories to Tell in the Dark by Alvin Schwartz
The Secret of Terror Castle by Robert Arthur
The 13th Floor: A Ghost Story by Sid Fleischman
Tituba of Salem Village by Ann Petry

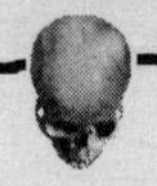

Learn from the Best

As you read each frightening tale, take note of how the author writes — the words he or she chooses, the characters, the details. Think about what makes the writing so good and scary. Start a collection of favorite lines or even favorite words, and write them down here.

Take a Closer Look

Now that you're familiar with the overall writing process, let's take a closer look at how to use words.

You can have the most spine-tingling plot ever created inside your head and still wind up with a so-so story unless you're able to express it well. By following some basic suggestions (and avoiding common mistakes), your stories will be frighteningly fantastic!

Stop the Echo

Can you tell what's wrong with the following paragraph?

> *Carl walked into the house. He stood at the bottom of the stairs and listened. He heard a creaking noise. He slowly started up the steps.*

Do you see a pattern here? If you noticed that three sentences begin with the word *he*, you're on the right track. This sort of repetition can result in a dull story.

Try your hand at rewriting this paragraph, avoiding the repetition. Use words such as since, before, after, instead, finally, meanwhile, when, later, *or* suddenly *to help you.*

____

____

____

____

____

____

____

____

____

____

Along the same lines, also try to avoid ending two or more sentences in a row with the same word. This sort of repetition can sound awkward or wrong to the ear. And don't forget the old trick of reading your work aloud — it can help you catch those repeated phrases and fix them.

Smooth Sailing

To keep your story flowing properly, be sure to avoid short, choppy sentences. Combining a group of very short sentences into one or two longer ones can keep the flow smooth. For example, see what you can do with the following sentences.

The ghost floated out of the trunk. It moved toward the window. The window was closed. The ghost lifted the window. It sailed out into the night air.

____

____

____

____

____

____

____

Try making use of such connecting words as *and, but, so, although*, and *as*. And don't forget commas, semicolons, and also periods to make your new sentences read correctly.

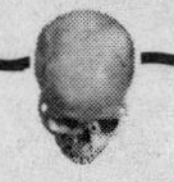

Showing vs. Telling

You may have heard the familiar writing rule, "Show, don't tell." This means you should use words to paint a picture in the reader's mind rather than simply telling that person a fact with no description.

Think about a spooky graveyard on a cold autumn evening. Taking the easiest way, you could simply tell your readers, "The graveyard was spooky and cold." But in order to create a clear, vivid image, you need to show that graveyard by using lots of detail and descriptive words.

For example:

> *As the wind whipped through the darkened graveyard, it sent dead leaves swirling among the headstones. The limbs of the ancient oak tree bent and swayed, casting long shadows like grasping hands against the moonlight. Somewhere in the distance, a lonely dog howled into the darkness.*

Get the idea? By adding detailed sights and sounds through strong descriptive images, you've made that graveyard come to life.

Become a Picasso

Using the rule of showing rather than telling, paint a written picture of one of the scenes below. Remember to make use of your five senses!

- **A dank, dark basement**
- **A deserted highway at midnight**
- **A remote cave filled with bats**
- **A jungle crawling with snakes and insects**
- **A broken-down shack in a forest**

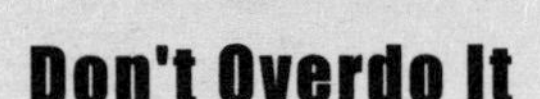

Don't Overdo It

Descriptive words such as adjectives and adverbs can be powerful tools when you want to convey a hair-raising image. For example:

The dog bared its razor-sharp teeth, thick strings of foam hanging from its muzzle. A deep growl rolled in its chest as its eyes glowed red in the dim light of the hall. Each wiry hair on the animal's back seemed to quiver. When the old wooden clock began to strike, the dog leaped toward the door.

As you see, descriptive words can make a scene seem as real as the paper on which it's printed. But there is also something known as too much of a good thing. Here's a sentence that tries a bit too hard.

The sad, low organ music echoed in the long, dark entryway as the vampire's cold white hand moved toward the old, heavy desk.

By being heavy-handed with adjectives, this sentence falls flat. Keep a balance in your writing, and each scene will come shining through.

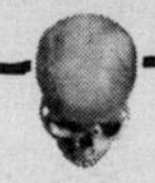

Weak Words

There are two words that you should try to avoid in your writing whenever possible. They are *really* and *very*.

Why use "Hayley was really scared" when "Hayley was terrified" can carry even more meaning? And why write "very old" when *ancient* or *decrepit* will work just as well?

Try making stronger word choices, and leave these overused ones behind. *Really* and *very* will thank you for the well-deserved rest!

Your Turn

Using all that you've learned about description, write any scary story you like on these pages. Remember to strike a balance, and choose your words carefully to make them leap off the page!

Simile Samples

Have you ever heard someone use the phrase "as silent as a tomb" or "hit like a ton of bricks"? If so, then you've heard a simile. Similes are comparisons of two things, using the words *like* or *as*.

Although they're not used as often as adjectives and adverbs, similes can produce strong images in the minds of your readers. For example, the sentence "He stared coldly at her" might be changed to "He stared at her with eyes as cold as ice." Likewise, "Her heart was broken" could become "Like a piece of shattered glass, her heart broke inside her chest."

See if you can rework one of the following sentences, using a simile of your own.

- **Ben ran across the empty field.**
- **A strong wind blew.**
- **Her hands held the book of spells.**

Mysterious Metaphors

A metaphor is much like a simile but without the *like* or *as* attached. So instead of the simile “Her heart was like a block of ice,” you would say “Her heart was a block of ice.”

You can have great fun with metaphors. “The fog was thick” can become “The fog was a heavy blanket on the meadow.” Or “The cat’s eyes glowed” might change to “The cat’s eyes were pieces of amber on fire.”

Try creating metaphors from the following sentences.

- **The rain is heavy.**
- **The thunder is loud.**
- **Her heart beat fast.**

Revise, Revise, Revise

Even if you're certain you've written an award-winning piece of frightening fiction, you must still take one final step before your work is complete: Go back and revise!

All writers begin with what is called a *first draft*. This is a rough copy, meant to be read and reread as you go through the revision process. You may want to set your first draft aside for a few days to remove yourself from the words for a while. Then when you come back to it, you may see it from a whole new angle.

Try asking a few questions when rereading and revising your work.

- **Does the plot make sense? Are there any holes or unanswered questions?**
- **Have I made good use of my words? Could there be a better word choice in any sentences?**
- **Does the story flow smoothly? Are there any slow or unnecessary parts that could come out?**
- **Have I developed characters the reader will care about and be interested in?**

And, of course, always be on the lookout for any misspellings and punctuation problems. Having a second set of eyes on your work can be a great help.

Try your hand at revising right now. Choose a piece of writing you did earlier in this book. Can you see any way to make it better? Use the following pages to try to improve your story.

Writing Groups and Classes

Being a writer can be a little isolating. That's why it can be helpful to join a writing group or take a writing class.

There may be writing groups that already exist in your community. Check with your school or library to find out. If there aren't any groups in your area, think about starting one of your own. Gather some friends who love writing scary stories as much as you do, and share your thoughts.

Writing groups meet to discuss the members' work and also to talk about any news in the field of writing. Group members may share book or author suggestions or even create reading lists and discuss a different title each time they meet.

A writing class given at a school, college, or community center can serve a similar purpose as a writing group. A class may be more structured than a group, and a helpful teacher can be an invaluable source of writing advice.

Whether you try a group or a class, remember that you are there to share thoughts and ideas. Although you may feel a bit intimidated at the thought of many people reading your stories, these groups are meant to provide support and guidance. No one's there to give harsh criticism or put anyone's writing down. So open your mind — and your notebook — and share your love of chilling tales!

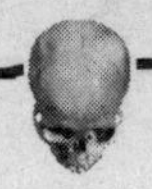

A Writer's Glossary

Action The middle part of a story where the characters try to deal with their problems

Character In a story, a person, animal, creature, or object with a personality

Climax The moment in a story when the characters solve their problem(s)

Dialogue Conversation between characters

Ending The final part of a story that ties up all loose ends

First person point of view A method of storytelling in which a character tells the story using *I* and *we*

Five senses The senses of sight, hearing, touch, taste, and smell that help a writer create a detailed image

Full circle The process of connecting a character's situation at the beginning of a story to his or her situation at the end

Journal A small, blank notebook used to record words, thoughts, stories, and ideas

Metaphor A figure of speech in which one word or phrase is used in place of another to suggest a likeness between the two (does not contain the words *like* or *as*)

Plot The main story, consisting of a setup, the action, and an ending

Red herrings Fake clues that a writer uses to confuse readers and create mystery or suspense

Setup The beginning part of a story in which the reader learns about the setting, the main character(s), and the character(s)' problem(s)

Setting Where and when a story takes place

Simile A comparison of two things using the words *like* or *as*

Third person point of view A method of storytelling in which an all-knowing narrator tells the story using *he*, *she*, and *they*

Turning point see **Climax**

Writing Resources

BOOKS

Bauer, Marion Dane. *What's Your Story? A Young Person's Guide to Writing Fiction.* Clarion Books, 1992.

Dahlstrom, Lorraine M. *Writing Down the Days: 365 Creative Journaling Ideas for Young People*. Free Spirit Publishing, 2000.

Fletcher, Ralph J. *How Writers Work: Finding a Process That Works for You*. HarperCollins Children's Books, 2000.

Fletcher, Ralph J. *Live Writing: Breathing Life Into Your Words*. Avon Books, 1999.

Grant, Janet E. *The Young Person's Guide to Becoming a Writer*. Free Spirit Publishing, 1995.

Mirriam-Goldberg, Caryn. *Write Where You Are: How to Use Writing to Make Sense of Your Life: A Guide for Teens*. Free Spirit Publishing, 1999.

New Moon Writing: How to Express Yourself with Passion and Practice. Crown Publishing, 2000.

Sebranek, Patrick. *Write Source 2000: A Guide to Writing, Thinking, and Learning*. D. C. Heath and Company, 1999.

Seuling, Barbara. *To Be a Writer: A Guide for Young People Who Want to Write and Publish.* Twenty-First Century Books, 1997.

Young, Sue. *Writing with Style*. Scholastic Inc., 1999.

MAGAZINES

The following magazines accept submissions from young writers. It's a good idea to write and ask for submission guidelines before you send your work.

American Girl. 8400 Fairway Place, Middleton, WI 53562

Blue Jean Magazine. 7353 Pittsford-Victor Road, Suite 201-203, Victor, NY 14564-9790

The Claremont Review: The International Magazine of Young Adult Writers. 4980 Wesley Road, Victoria, BC V8Y 1Y9, CANADA

Creative Kids. P.O. Box 8813, Waco, TX 76714

Highlights for Children. 803 Church Street, Honesdale, PA 18431

Merlyn's Pen: The National Magazine of Student Writing. P.O. Box 1058, East Greenwich, RI 02818

Skipping Stones: A Multicultural Children's Magazine. P.O. Box 3939, Eugene, OR 97403

Stone Soup: The Magazine by Young Writers and Artists. Children's Art Foundation, P.O. Box 83, Santa Cruz, CA 95063

TeenInk: Written Entirely by Teens for Teens. Box 30, Newton, MA 02101

Teen Voices: Because You're More Than Just a Pretty Face. Women Express, Inc. P.O. Box 120-027, Boston, MA 02112-0027

360 Degrees: The Magazine with Every Angle. P.O. Box 25356, Washington, DC 20007

Word Dance: The Magazine Dedicated to the Voice of Today's Youth. 59 Pavilions Drive, Manchester, CT 06040

Writes of Passage: The Literary Journal for Teenagers. 817 Broadway, 6th floor, New York, NY 10003

Young Voices Magazine: The Magazine of Young People's Creative Work. P.O. Box 2321, Olympia, WA 98507

WEB SITES

This list of Web sites is a brief guide to Internet resources for and by young writers. As the fast-paced world of the Internet seems to change hourly, this list may quickly become outdated. Try searching *writing by kids, creative writing for kids,* and *young writers' resources* to find up-to-date sites.

Children's Writing
http://www.acs.ucalgary.ca/~dkbrown/writings.html

Cyberkids
http://www.cyberkids.com

Kidstuff
http://www.kidstuff.org

Merlyn's Pen
http://www.merlynspen.com

Stone Soup
http://www.stonesoup.com

TeenInk: Written Entirely by Teens for Teens
http://www.teenpaper.org

Teen Voices: Because You're More Than Just a Pretty Face
http://www.teenvoices.com

Writes of Passage: The Literary Journal for Teenagers
http://www.writes.org